Self-Transformation
through
Transformational Yoga

All Life is Yoga

- Sri Aurobindo

Om

Ananda mayee
She, the Delight

Chaitanya mayee
She, the Consciousness

Satya mayee
She, the Truth

Paramee
She, the Supreme

Self-Transformation
through
Transformational Yoga

Swami Vidyanand

Founder

Transformational Yoga

STERLING PAPERBACKS
An imprint of
Sterling Publishers (P) Ltd.
Regd. Office: A1/256 Safdarjung Enclave,
New Delhi-110029. Cin: U22110DL1964PTC211907
Tel: 26387070, 26386209; Fax: 91-11-26383788
E-mail: mail@sterlingpublishers.com
www.sterlingpublishers.com

SELF-TRANSFORMATION THROUGH TRANSFORMATIONAL YOGA
© 2015, © SriMA International School of Transformational Yoga
ISBN 978 81 207 9603 4
Revised Edition 2017

Disclaimer
The information presented here is for informational purpose. The user of this information accepts all responsibility for practising the techniques described here. It is advisable to consult a doctor before undertaking strenuous physical activities such as Yoga. Please also keep in mind that Transformational Yoga is not a substitute for medical care or physiotherapy.

PRINTED IN INDIA

Printed and Published by Sterling Publishers Pvt. Ltd., Plot No. 13, Ecotech-III, Greater Noida - 201306, Uttar Pradesh, India

This book is dedicated to
The Mother and Sri Aurobindo

Contents

Preface

This book provides the methodology for a fast-track and multidimensional self-purification, which is the core theory that underpins the practice. To yoga practitioners, some of this will be familiar, some will be new.

Why is this important? In short, it enables direct connection with the higher self, bringing true wisdom and enlightenment. During this time, your focus is on your 'inner self'. The practice is simple and can be followed by people of all ages and body types.

It is very important that one tries to focus on the 'inner self', as it will soon follow, that after purifying this, your 'external life' will also benefit. This is the development of true inner wisdom which adds to your personal magnetism. For most people, the practice takes between 10 and 40 days to complete, depending on the individual practitioner and their state of readiness. The words are, of course, only the starting point - after that it is up to the individual to make this happen, and it will take discipline, time, concentration, and hard work.

Swami Vidyanand

Introduction: Transformational Yoga

Transformational Yoga is an integral approach to physical health, emotional balance, mental and spiritual clarity.

Transformational Yoga gives you the tools you need in order to make a difference in your everyday life. In-depth focus of asanas, the chakras, mantras, breathing and meditation techniques gives you the knowledge you need to purify your body, stabilise your emotions, focus your mind, and increase your spiritual well-being.

Transformational Yoga is a truly modern avatar of traditional practices.

It goes far beyond just physical exercise. While offering a complete approach to well-being, Transformational Yoga takes into account physical, emotional, mental and spiritual aspects of health. It functions on a deeper level to stimulate kundalini energy to move up through the chakras, purifying and awakening the pure body.

It synthesises techniques of a variety of yogic systems to bring about rapid transformation, awakening all five bodies and seven chakras in order to experience a continuous state of physical health and stamina, emotional balance, higher mental guidance, unconditional love , faith and spiritual bliss consciousness.

In Transformational Yoga the following techniques are applied in order to accomplish personal transformation:

The asana sequences are suitable for everyone from beginners to advanced and offer a holistic approach to health, while focusing on chakra activation, back strengthening, stomach strengthening and a standing series.

Pranayama breathing techniques are an essential component of Hatha Yoga. Discover the healing potential of your breath. Benefits include improved concentration, more energy, deeper sleep, and reduced stress levels. Not only does it feed the brain, but revitalises the body, since breath is the bridge between the body and the mind.

Mantra chanting generates vibrations which are fundamental tools for altering the psyche, and producing a tranquil and balanced mind. In yogic practices, the growth of our awareness progresses with the help of these vibrations. By cleansing our minds with mantras, decision making becomes clearer and observation power is sharpened. This leads to improved concentration and a calm focused mind.

There is a Supreme Divine Consciousness. We want to manifest this Divine Consciousness in the physical life.

Blessings

Meditation, yoga nidra, and other relaxation techniques are included in the Transformational Yoga practice in order for us to experience our pure nature, in which our ego dissolves and we find inner silence and peace.

"With Transformational Yoga, one can relax, clean and awaken all seven chakras through yogasana, pranayama, mantra and meditation."

The focus is on creating full awareness of each of our five bodies.

In doing so we are able to clear blockages and purify ourselves. We learn about the seven chakras, and their relationships to our five bodies, whilst identifying and clearing blockages in the chakras.

Transformational Yoga is for all kinds of people—corporates, children and young people, the aged and for women during and after pregnancy. For specific issues such as reproductive difficulties or terminal diseases, it is a powerful tool of healing.

Transformational Yoga is inspired by Sri Aurobindo and The Mother.

SriMa - The Mother - is the inspiring fountainhead of all that is taught at SriMa International School of Transformational Yoga.

"From the point of view of a spiritual life, it is not what you do that matters most, but the way in which it is done and the consciousness you put into it. Remember always the Divine and all you do will be an expression of the Divine Presence. When all your actions are consecrated to the Divine, there will be no longer activities that are superior and activities that are inferior; all will have an equal importance - the value given them by the consecration."

- The Mother

Theory of Transformational Yoga: Connecting to the Higher Self

This system of purification focuses on intensive cleaning of the four lower chakras—our 'false' un-transformed (apara) self. This enables energy to be released to the four higher chakras— our pure, transformed (para) soul, and thereby connection to be made to the higher self.

> *Sri Aurobindo explains in his book The Life Divine that both un-transformed and transformed souls exist at the same time in all humans - we are born with a double soul.*

Upon the death of the physical body, the un-transformed, apara soul is also destroyed—it is finite, for this life only. The transformed, para soul is eternal, and continues to exist in other dimensions.

Enlightenment through yoga not only enables us to achieve this 'final' transformation mindfully, but also to live our journey in this current life time in a more meaningful way. Enlightenment means connection with our inner guide, the ability to follow our chosen path using intuition, and to learn and develop spiritually.

Transformational Yoga is rooted within this philosophy.

Basic Anatomy of Transformational Yoga

Chakras

Sahasrara is the 7th chakra located just above the crown of the head.
- **Creator of the transformed physical body.**
- The seat of enlightenment.
- Space element

Ajna is the 6th chakra located between the eyebrows—the 'third eye'.
- **Creator of the transformed prana body.**
- Associated with inner vision, willpower and high immunity.
- **Space element**

Vishuddhi is the 5th chakra located at the throat.
- **Creator of the transformed mental body.**
- Associated with inner guidance and wisdom, expression and clarity.
- Space element

Anahata is the 4th chakra located behind the heart.
A double chakra, made up of the **Lower Anahata** and **Higher Anahata**.
- **Creator of the un-transformed and transformed psychic bodies.**
- Associated with emotional attachments, love and relationships.
- **Air element**

Manipura is the 3rd chakra located behind the navel.
- **Creator of the un-transformed mental body.**
- Associated with the ego and mental energy.
- Fire element

Swadisthana is the 2nd chakra located in the lower abdomen.
- Associated with blind emotions such as anger, fear, jealousy and lust.
- **Creator of the un-transformed prana body.**
- Water element

Mooladhara is the 1st chakra located at the perineum.
- Associated with basic survival, safety and security issues.
- **Creator of the un-transformed physical body.**
- **Earth element**

15

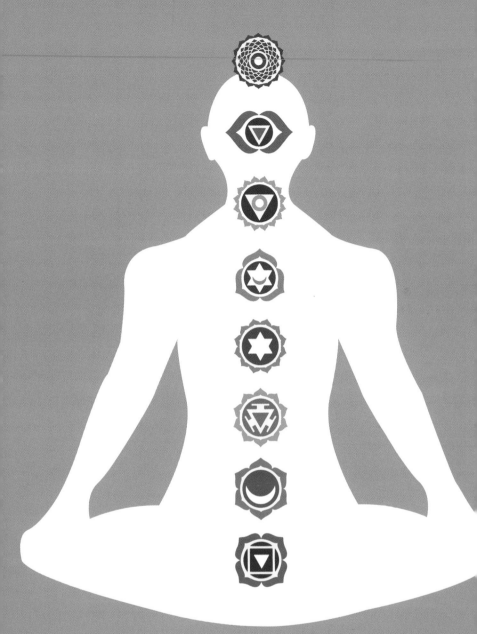

The chakras are energy centres that process, store and distribute pure energy around the body. The positions of the chakras coincide with the positions of the nerve plexuses along the spinal cord in the physical body. When these powerful energy centres are purified and activated good physical health, emotional balance and spiritual well-being will develop.

The Five Bodies

Body	About	Untransformed Characteristics
Physical Body	Concerned with physical aspects of life and survival. Represents the densest form of energy in the solid state. It is connected with the earth element.	Diseases in organs which have accumulation of impurities or imbalance of energy, which are caused by unhealthy food, smoking, alcohol, lack of sleep, overeating, exercise, etc. For example, obesity, lethargy.
Prana Body	Concerned with sexuality, lower emotions and vitality. Houses powerful blind emotions such as lust, jealousy, desire, possessiveness, anger and fear. It represents the fluid form of energy which is evident in the high percentage of liquid that constitutes the body. It is connected with the water element.	When purified, we have control of these lower emotions. Diseases in organs which have accumulation of impure energies in the form of unexpressed emotions, e.g. pancreas (diabetes), sexual organs (infertility, impotence, menstrual problems, etc), chest (asthma, hypertension and heart diseases).
Mental Body	Concerned with thoughts, personality, ego, wisdom, intellect, memory and imagination. Responsible for feelings of superiority/inferiority and the power we exert over others. Connected with the fire element. When purified, improves our interpersonal relations and personality.	Diseases in organs which have accumulation of impure energies in the form of unexpressed thoughts, planning, collection of negative thoughts/complexes through feeling superior/inferior or inability to accept situations, e.g. stomach related problems, headaches, depression.
Psychic Body	Concerned with heart orientated, higher emotions and spirituality. Evident through our spiritual aspirations. Governs our response to love and religion. Connected to the air element. When purified gives ability to love unconditionally.	Diseases in organs which have accumulation of impure heart orientated emotional energy blocks, e.g. disappointments (unrequited love), pain associated with human relationships. Inability to give or receive love, diseases of the heart and lungs and suicidal tendencies.
Spiritual Body	Connected with highest level of wisdom and source of pure consciousness, leading to truth and infinity. Evident in search for self-realisation, giving us freedom from desires and bondage of lower nature. When activated, we experience pure bliss, love, harmony, beauty, peace, knowledge and power. Connected to space and light.	Completely transformed, hence no un-transformed characteristics.

17

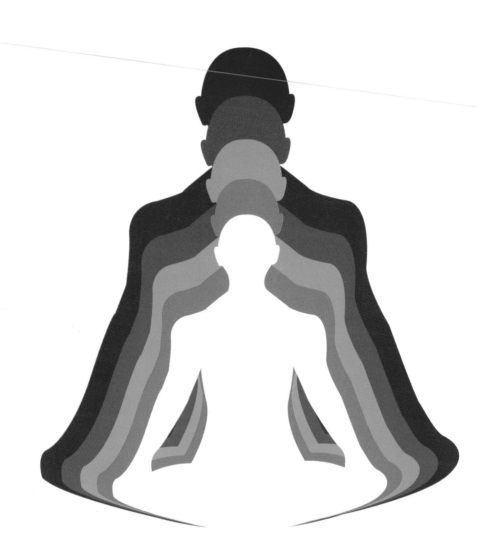

Yoga's holistic model of the human system is called the Panchakosha concept, taken from The Upanashad; pancha means five, kosha means layer. The five unique aspects of the personality—body, breath, mind, wisdom and bliss—interact in order to integrate consciousness and energy into a harmonious human being, resulting in balance and health.

The Five Pranas

The five pranas are profoundly affected by lifestyle. Physical activities like sleep, work, exercise, diet, sex, thought and emotion, all affect the flow of prana in the body. You can feel drained of energy when irregularities in lifestyle, diet and stress deplete or block the pranic flow. If this continues it may lead to disease and dysfunction in the particular areas of the body where the pranic flow is most obstructed. Pranayama techniques help to reverse this process, energising and balancing the pranas.

Name	ACTIVITY
VYANA PRANA	Working through the nervous system, vyana prana is the energy network that links all the chakras. Any benefit from powerful exercises or kriyas are useless if vyana prana is weak, as the energy created does not get distributed to the other bodies. This exercise helps to balance the sun and moon energies.
UDANA PRANA	Located in the head and neck areas, udana prana is connected to vishuddhi, ajna and sahasrara chakras. It flows in an upward direction. It controls also the five senses and the actions of the limbs. All forms of higher consciousness experiences (samadhi, kundalini, etc) are only possible with its activation.
MAHA PRANA	Connected to anahata chakra, maha prana flows in an upward direction (like fire). On the physical plane, it controls the functions of the heart, lungs and the respiratory system and regulates blood circulation. It maintains the emotional balance within the body. On the mental plane, it develops logical abilities and clarity. At the psychic level it produces the healing and supernatural energies.
SAMANA PRANA	It is the mental prana, situated in the stomach area, and is connected to manipura chakra. It flows in a circular direction. It controls the digestive system and governs the storage, production and distribution of energy from food.
APANA PRANA	Situated in the hip area, apana prana is connected to mooladhara and swadhisthana chakras. It flows down towards the earth. On the physical plane it governs the release of toxins (sweat, faeces, urine). If it is weak in a person, detoxification will not be successful. At the emotional level it creates excitement.

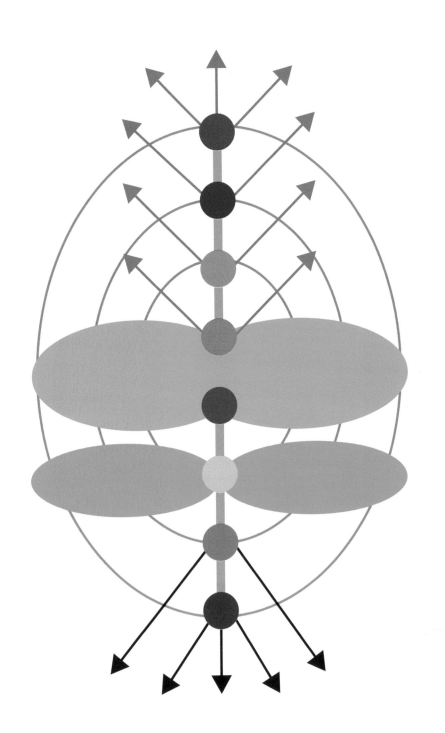

Nadis

The word 'nadi' means flow—in this sense the nadis are subtle flows of energy relating to the energy body, as the nerves which are located in the physical body. They are pathways of pranic, mental and spiritual currents, numbering anywhere between 72,000 and 350,000 according to ancient yogic texts.

The main nadis are **Ida**, **Pingala** and **Sushumna**; they all originate from mooladhara chakra, the root chakra. Pingala curves to the right, then follows its path, changing sides at each intersection with Ida until it reaches Ajna; Ida follows the opposite path, and Sushumna goes straight up through the centre, all meeting together at Ajna, from where they travel directly to Sahasrara.

IDA	SHUSHUMNA	PINGALA
Left side of body	Central column	Right side of body
Right brain hemisphere	Neutral	Left brain hemisphere
Cold	Neutral	Hot
Lunar (Chandra)	Neutral	Solar (Surya)
Relaxation	Neutral	Physical vitality
Sedentary activity	Neutral	Dynamic activity
Passivity	Neutral	Tension
Mental and psychic	Neutral	Physical and prana

Sushumna is the most important nadi in the subtle body; from mooladhara chakra it travels slightly to the rear and upwards to swadhisthana chakra, from where it travels through the spinal column via Manipura, Anahata and Vishuddhi chakras until it reaches that point in the lower brain where the spinal column ends; from there it travels straight upwards through Ajna and Bindu chakras, finishing at the top of Sahasrara.

Mooladhara Chakra

Position	1st chakra
Sanskrit meaning	Moola: 'root' or 'foundation'
Main purpose	Creation of physical body
Physical location	Female: at base of the cervix, male: at the perineum
Kshetram (trigger point)	Female: at base of the cervix, male: at perineum
Subtle body (kosha)	Impure/un-transformed physical body
Element	Earth
Connected with	Sahasrara (7th chakra)
Prana relationship	Apana
Sense	Smell
Sense organ	Nose
Action organ	Anus
Source of energy	Food and sleep
Objective	To live
Example	Plant
Activity	Hatha Yoga

Ten percent of the energy generated by Mooladhara is used in the creation of the physical body—bones, skin and so on—90% is unused and inactive, collecting at the base of the spinal cord in the centre of Mooladhara Chakra. This is the source of Kundalini. Adult humans tend not to express all their energy, compared with animals who instinctively release their energy through movement; so pockets of impure, unexpressed energy tend to be created around the physical body. Because physical energy is generated through food and sleep, and only about 50% of our food energy is normally expressed through physical activity, this can lead to extra fat cells, as this energy is being stored and not used or released. So the normal mooladhara produces energy through food, and this energy - following the laws of nature—wants to be distributed and not to be held. However, Mooladhara chakra wants all the energy retained and held in the physical body.

The aim of Hatha Yoga is to activate the 90% and generate this Kundalini energy, which can be done through any yogic method— asana, pranayama, etc. It is still possible to connect with the Divine without focussing any attention on cleaning the physical body—witness many great masters who connect with the Divine with great joy and forget about their physical body, so collecting these pockets of impure energy around them, often manifested as extra fat. Yogic energy of Mooladhara is blind, and in itself it has no wisdom.

If you have too much unexpressed physical energy the symptoms are clear: you like and crave spicy foods, alcohol and smoking; you tend to be lazy, sleep a lot and get tired quickly. If you clean the physical pockets carefully, then no mental effort is needed to stop these addictions—it follows automatically, the bad habit(s) stop and you can feel the difference—you feel lighter.

A key question is how to effectively generate the energy through asanas. There is a natural law which requires balance in all things—matter and anti-matter, positive and negative - and in this case un-transformed and transformed energy, para and apara, finite and eternal. So the law dictates that the levels of un-transformed and transformed energy are maintained in a state of balance - both are needed, both play their part, and you can change this balance to achieve higher levels of transformed energy through yogic practices. Hatha yoga addresses matter, and how to generate Kundalini energy thereby achieving higher consciousness; as it is released, the heat of the energy rises, and connects with Sahasrara, which is in a frozen state, the heat acts as a catalyst to release and purify this energy.

Purification of Mooladhara Chakra

The purification process for Mooladhara chakra is based on cleaning the pockets of toxins—stuck energy—in the physical body. This is achieved through carrying out the full sequence of asanas used in transformational yoga, holding the stretch whilst observing and focussing your mind on pockets of stuck energy which are experienced as areas of pain or pressure. The asana is held as long as needed, and then released. Inner wisdom will guide you through this process and you will become accustomed to recognising which areas to focus on, how long to hold and when to release.

Swadisthana Chakra

Position	2nd chakra
Sanskrit meaning	Swa: 'one's own', adhisthana: 'dwelling place'
Main purpose	Creation of the prana body
Physical location	Base of spine on the coccyx
Kshetram (trigger point)	On front of the body at hara point (3 fingers down from navel)
Subtle body (kosha)	Impure/untransformed prana (vital) body
Element	Water
Connected with	Ajna (6th chakra)
Prana relationship	Apana Prana and Vyana Prana
Sense	Taste
Sense organ	Tongue
Action organ	Sexual organs, kidneys, urinary system
Source of energy	Breath, relationships
Objective	To survive
Example	Animal
Activity	Pranayama

Swadhisthana chakra is the power house of energy; it expands when a person is happy, and shrinks when they are sad. When it shrinks, the physical body loses its protection and is open to the entry of viruses and infections. So it is crucial in maintaining the body's immune system, which means that if prana is weak, the immune system is compromised.

As with Mooladhara chakra, only 10% of available energy has been used to create the prana body, and 90% of the energy remains inside. Pranayama generates yogic energy to the second chakra, and expands the prana body. Additionally, any other kind of yogic exercise will generate energy in this body.

An indicator of the essential nature of prana to life is demonstrated by the extreme sensitivity of the hara point to any physical impact—a punch in the stomach (which we might refer to as 'being winded') can be so serious that if it removes prana energy stored there it can lead to death.

The unexpressed energy pockets which relate to this chakra are due to blind emotions being stored up, such as fear, attachment, anger, jealousy, animal type emotions which are not easily expressed by humans in day to day life. For example, we may resent being instructed what to do, and this may make us angry, but we cannot express our anger because we respect or fear the individual. This energy collects and sticks in the Swadishtana region, chest and throat.

Purification of Swadishthana Chakra

It is important to remember that for this purification process, the focus at this time is not on generating energy, but just on cleaning out the pockets of impure energy. Whilst holding the asanas as set out for cleaning Mooladhara (see below) carry out gentle kapalbhati (rapid exhale) breathing - not forceful, using only about 30% of breath. Assume the posture, observe your prana body, then do Kapalbhati breathing with particular focus on any areas of pain or pressure until you feel this released.

Manipura Chakra

Position	3rd chakra
Sanskrit meaning	Mani: 'jewel', pura: 'city'
Main purpose	Creation of the mental body
Physical location	Behind the navel on the inner wall of the spinal column
Kshetram (trigger point)	On front of the body at the navel
Subtle body (kosha)	Impure/un-transformed mental body
Element	Fire
Connected with	Vishuddhi (5th chakra)
Prana relationship	Samana Prana
Sense	Sight
Sense organ	Eyes
Action organ	Feet
Objective	To succeed
Example	Human being
Activity	Raja Yoga

Manipura chakra has a three dimensional structure: past, present and future. The 'past mind' creates our mental image, and our memories create our mental ego, all of which lead to our self-image and how we define ourselves. This is completely subjective, involving, for example, our association with work, and how superior or inferior we see ourselves in relation to others. An example of how toxins accumulate in this area is that this relative sense of status leads the 'future mind' to plan how to improve our position, and increase our feelings of superiority. When these plans fail—as they often do—our reaction to and reflections on these failures create unexpressed or stuck thought pockets around the mental area - impure mental energy.

The present dimension of the mind has wisdom, and this is what we aspire to achieve through following the cleaning process outlined below. Again, only 10% of the energy is active, with 90% sleeping and unused. The process of self-observation helps to release and utilise this dormant energy, increasing intelligence and enabling mental clarity and intuition. The constant external focus and information overload in our current culture reduces energy, diminishes intelligence, and leads to a draining of energy through activities such as office work, computers, watching TV, movies, etc.

Energy is subject to the universal laws of balance, so that if two people with different energy levels are together and communicating, the higher level goes down and the lower goes up. This is something to be aware of, particularly when you are striving to maintain your energy levels.

Purification of Manipura Chakra

As before, whilst holding each posture the method this time is Bhramari (hummingbee's breath). The sound waves go inside the mind, driving out unexpressed thoughts and creating space within the mind for intelligent thought. You need to repeat Bhramari more than 3 times to achieve self cleaning, and yet again, allow yourself to be guided by your inner wisdom about how long to hold each posture to clean the stuck mental energy.

 **Anahata Chakra**

Position	4th chakra
Sanskrit meaning	'unstruck' or 'unbeaten' - centre of unbroken rhythm of the heart
Main purpose	Creation of the psychic body
Physical location	On inner wall of the spinal column behind centre of the chest
Kshetram (trigger point)	On front of the body at the sternum
Subtle body (kosha)	Transformed and un-transformed psychic body
Element	Air
Connected with	Inner anahata (Higher heart chakra)
Prana relationship	Maha Prana
Sense	Touch
Sense organ	Skin
Action organ	Hands
Objective	Harmony
Example	Integral human being
Activity	Bhakti Yoga

Anahata chakra is about love, happiness, human relationships, expectations—in its apara (impure) aspect this is conditional love, love which makes us dependent on the objects of our affections. Focussing on the un-transformed aspect (apara), the toxins that gather here as pockets of unexpressed energy in the heart/chest area, stem from disappointments, rejection and other hurts arising from our intimate relationships, often referred to colloquially as a 'broken heart'.

The un-transformed Anahata Chakra is the seat of love, but with conditions. If blocked, the person becomes hurtful, selfish and uncompassionate. While those with a helpful nature, one of kindness, compassion and love have an active Anahata. However, this love too is laid with conditions or expectations and when these are not met with, they lead to disappointment or hurt, resulting in an accumulation of stuck energy in the Anahata Chakra.

The Higher or Transformed Anahata chakra has no expectations or conditions. It remains loving even if it does not receive anything in return. If active, the person has love not only for his near and dear ones, but for all mankind and all things living and manifest in the universe. This is the love that is spoken of as Divine love when referring to the Buddhas and sages or avatars that is often spoken of in sacred texts. The Transformed heart chakra is the manifestation of the Divine love in human form.

Purification of Anahata Chakra

As before, holding each posture and chanting OMA several times, holding and chanting for as long as you feel is needed.

Vishuddhi Chakra

Position	5th chakra
Sanskrit meaning	Centre of Nectar
Main purpose	Creation of the pure mental body
Physical location	Throat region
Kshetram (trigger point)	Throat pit
Subtle body (kosha)	Transformed Mental Body
Element	Transformed Fire
Connected with	Manipura (3rd Chakra)
Prana relationship	Udana Prana
Action organ	Voice box
Source of energy	Universal Mind
Objective	To provide right guidance
Example	Awakened Human
Gland	Thyroid Gland

 **Ajna Chakra**

Position	6th chakra
Sanskrit meaning	Command Centre
Main purpose	Creation of the pure prana body
Physical location	Eyebrow Centre
Kshetram (trigger point)	Eyebrow centre
Subtle body (kosha)	Transformed prana (vital) body
Element	Transformed Water
Connected with	Swadishthana (2nd chakra)
Prana relationship	Udana Prana
Action organ	Universal Network of energy
Source of energy	Universal Vital
Objective	Intuition
Example	Awakened Human
Gland	Pituitary

Sahasrara Chakra

Position	7th chakra
Sanskrit meaning	Infinity centre
Main purpose	Creation of the pure physical body
Physical location	Crown
Kshetram (trigger point)	Crown
Subtle body (kosha)	Transformed Physical Body
Element	Transformed Earth
Connected with	Mooladhara (1st Chakra)
Prana relationship	Udana
Source of energy	Cosmos
Objective	Astral travel, beyond the body
Example	Awakened Human
Gland	Pineal Gland

Para and Apara Bodies

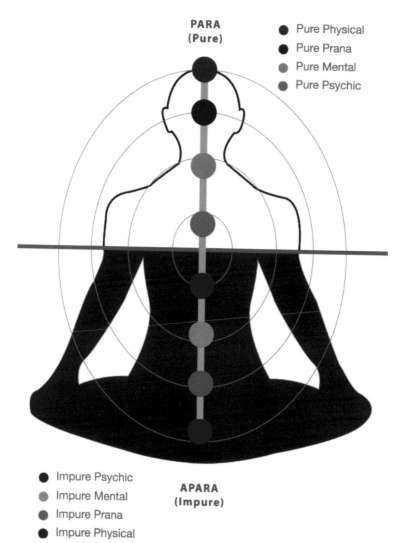

PARA
(Pure)

● Pure Physical
● Pure Prana
● Pure Mental
● Pure Psychic

● Impure Psychic
● Impure Mental
● Impure Prana
● Impure Physical

APARA
(Impure)

Para – Transformed Consciousness, often refers to the four higher chakras

Apara – Un-transformed consciousness, often refers to the four lower chakras

In his book, *The Life Divine,* Sri Aurobindo refers to the concept of "Double Soul". To summarize, he talks about the two polar opposites of creation. For every right guidance or decision, there is also the polar opposite, and both are working inside us. The PARA (pure) and the APARA (impure).

The Higher chakras are always in active state, but are not accessible since we have too many toxins or too much stuck energy blocking the path ways in different bodies, hence, we cannot make decisions or perform actions from the higher chakras. Through the practice of Transformational Yoga, one can remove the stuck energy of the lower chakras and hence prepare the pathways to receive energy from the higher chakras. Activating one's spiritual fire and cleaning the lower chakras, melts the ice around the higher chakras and then one is able to function from higher states of consciousness.

Mind and Meditation

Aspects of the Mind

Mind is the medium via which consciousness can communicate with the self. Since there is consciousness in all things, similarly there is a mind in all our bodies, and it helps us to communicate with each other and the self, according to the individual's level of consciousness.

According to this system, the human mind can be divided into four:

Physical Mind: It is the mind of the Physical body and the physical dimension of our existence. Asanas help clean not just the physical body, but the Physical Mind as well.

Prana Mind: It is the mind of the Prana body and the vital dimension. Pranayama helps clean not just the prana body, but the prana mind also.

Mental Mind: It is the mind of the Mental body. Observation, mantras and meditation are some ways to purify the mental mind.

Psychic Mind: It is the mind of the Psychic body. Invoking the Divine, love, surrender and faith are some ways to transform the psychic mind.

All these minds together shape the Mental body, to make decisions according to the individual's requirement in the given space and time.

WHAT IS MEDITATION?

Meditation is the science-experienced process of communication with the purest, highest consciousness. It is expressed in experience, and expressed in practical life, creating peaceful harmony in our relationships, in everything that we do.

Meditation gives complete respect to all religions, however is not a religion in itself.

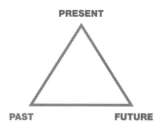

PRESENT

PAST   FUTURE

Past	Present	Future
• Power of memory/power to forget • Forms our "knowledge" from books, conditioned thought processes + personal experiences. These are not always true as facts taught or conditioning may be wrong) • Forms ego which gives our "self-image" i.e. who we think we are - his may be false as it may be based on nationality, social/financial status, etc. • Leads to inferiority or superiority • Leads to dissatisfaction or the urge to better ourselves based on false assumptions of money, success, material things, etc. • Memory has 4 dimensions: 1. Physical > smell/visual 2. Vital > anger, fears 3. Mental > study, past learning, conditioning etc. 4. Psychic > Parents, family, love etc.	• Here lies our power of wisdom + true guidance exists in this dimension • Intelligence/power to grasp and understand, knowledge, intellect, clarity, focus, power of observation • If we develop this dimension, we develop and activate our true guidance power and wisdom. • True Knowledge awakens (not dependent on facts, memory or conditioning) • LIGHT + TRUTH = CAN RECEIVE TRUE GUIDANCE POWER • TRUE MEDITATION IS HERE > Leads to enlightenment > Light + truth + wisdom + true knowledge • FULL AWARENESS Example: Science, Ayurveda knowledge comes through observation and awareness techniques, laws are discovered, Science and Yoga is born • DYNAMIC MEDITATION METHOD FOR REMAINING IN THE PRESENT > Practice of Transformational Yoga / Meditation > Practical Life Meditation: Observing your physical, vital, mental and psychic bodies/ habits at all times can transform energy or consciousness > Observe: "Who is Observing" > You awaken your true being (no inferiority or superiority with constant joy and bliss)	• Imagination Power • This is often false as it is based on events or things that have not yet happened or may not even happen. • Leads to wrong guidance power. • Leads to Dreams/Visions (When one's true guidance is activated, one has the power to see the future / visions).

Bandhas and Yog Nidra

Bandhas

Bandhas "the Locks" are special bodily manoeuvres that aim to confine the prana within the torso and redirect its flow into the Sushumna nadi for the purpose of spiritual awakening. The Bandhas act directly upon the 3 Granthis "knots", which block the flow of prana and impede the rising of Kundalini.

Moola Bandha: Root Lock

Method I: Gently clench and pull upwards and inwards the cervix/perineum centre and release.

Method II: Inhale and Gently clench and pull upwards and inwards the cervix centre, Exhale and release.

Method III: Inhale and Gently clench and pull upwards and inwards the cervix centre, Hold the breath and keep the cervix clenched, Exhale and release the lock.

Note: Do not strain or use force, always remain relaxed.

Benefits: • Increases the flow of Apana Prana • Awakens Mooladhara Chakra • Energy is released and can move up from the 1st Chakra to the 7th Chakra - This energy can be used for spiritual purpose or for the enhancement of sexual relations • Relieves depression • Stimulates pelvic nerves • Tones the Uro-genital and excretory system • Relieves psychosomatic illnesses • Helps realign the physical, mental and psychic bodies • Brahma Granthi - the 1st knot can be loosened or opened, allowing Kundalini energy to move upwards • Releases blind emotions and suppressed energy in the prana Body and Swadishthana Chakra

Udiyana Bandha: Abdominal Contraction

Method I: Inhale from the nose, complete exhalation through the mouth (blowing the air out) while simultaneously pulling the navel inwards. After complete exhalation, inhale through the nose and allow the navel to return to its normal position.

Method II: Inhale from the nose, complete exhalation through the mouth (blowing the air out) while simultaneously pulling the navel inwards, after complete exhalation, hold the breath and the navel in for a short duration, inhale through the nose and allow the navel to return to it normal position.

Benefits: • Purifies toxins from all four bodies by generating heat, hence, space is created for energy to rise • Increases the flow of Samana Prana • Increases the digestive fire • Massages, tones and strengthens the digestive organs • Adrenal Glands are balanced • Improved blood circulation in the torso • Reverses the flow of Apana Prana, hence uniting it with the active Samana • Stimulates the 3rd Chakra • Vishnu Granthi - loosens the psychic knot associated with the 3rd and 4th Chakras • Connects the Impure Mind (3rd Chakra) to the Pure Mind (5th Chakra). Once the Vishnu Granthi is transcended, one is no longer bound by physical, mental and emotional attachments • Relations and energies become more universal

Jalandhara Bandha: Throat Lock

Method I: Touch the chin to the chest, and begin Ujjayi Breath - (tighten the muscles around the throat pit), release after a few moments.

Method II: Touch the chin to the chest, and begin Ujjayi Breath - (tighten the muscles around the throat pit), hold for short duration while putting physical pressure by pressing down against both knees, and release the breath after a few moments, while raising your head.

Benefits: • Balances the Thyroid gland • Regulates Metabolism • Calms the mind • Relieves stress, anxiety and anger • Develops concentration • The four bodies are activated and spiritual energy is increased • Rudra Granthi - the 3rd knot is loosened, activating the Pure Prana and Pure Mental Bodies. When transcended, one's individuality is left behind and one becomes Universal.

Maha Bandha: The Great Lock

Method: Inhale from the nose, exhaling 1st apply Moolbandha, then add Udiyana Bandha followed by Jaladhara Bandha, hold for desired duration, exhaling 1st release Jaladhara Bandha, then release Udiyana Bandha and lastly release Moolbandha.

Note: The application and release of Mahabandha should be in a flow, like a domino effect. Pause between rounds to experience and observe the effects on the 4 bodies.

Benefits: • Accelerates Spiritual progress • Gives enhanced benefits of all 3 Bandhas • Balances the hormonal secretions of the Penial Gland • Regulates the whole endocrine system • Body is rejuvenated • Aging process is delayed • Prepares the mind for mediation • Activates Kundalini energy • Activates all bodies and all chakras • Leads to higher states of consciousness and bliss

Yog Nidra

When the chattering mind is stopped, and senses withdrawn, inner peace will follow.

Yog Nidra is a powerful technique in which you can learn to relax consciously. For true relaxation, you must remain aware, in a dynamic state of sleep. It is a systematic method of inducing complete physical, mental and emotional relaxation. During this practice one seems to be asleep, but the consciousness is functioning at a deeper level of awareness. In this state between sleep and wakefulness, contact with the subconscious and unconscious dimensions automatically occurs. If the consciousness can be separated from the external awareness and from sleep, it may be applied in many ways such as: transforming one's nature, increasing knowledge, creativity and boosting memory.

When the relaxation is complete, the receptivity is greater. But when the consciousness is connected to all the senses in a wakeful state, receptivity is less. Therefore, when you withdraw your mind a bit and enter into a state where you are neither in deep sleep nor completely awake, whatever impressions enter the mind become powerful and they remain there.

If you have habits you wish to overcome or goals you want to reach, you should put sankalpas into the unconscious and then listen to them during conscious state. Sankalpa is a Sanskrit word meaning resolve or resolution. It is an important part of yog nidra and a powerful tool to reshape your personality and move your life in a positive direction. The resolve made at the beginning is like planting a powerful seed in the subconscious, it then gathers power in the mind and starts to manifest at a conscious level in your everyday life.

THE THREE LEVELS OF TENSION

Yogic philosophy and modern psychology agree that there are three basic types of tension which are responsible for the agonies of life. The systematic practice of Yog Nidra works on all three levels of tension in order to release built up stress.

Muscle Tension: this is related to the physical body, the nervous system and endocrine imbalances. This type of tension is easily removed by the deep physical relaxation reached in Yog Nidra.

Emotional Tension: These are more of a challenge to get rid of. They come from various dualities such as love and hate, success and failure, happiness and sadness, etc. Emotions become repressed when we do not express them freely or recognize them, resulting in the tensions becoming deep rooted. Yog Nidra can be useful in tranquillizing the entire emotional structure of the mind so that these blocked emotions can be expressed.

Mental Tension: This results from too much mental activity. These accumulated tensions of the mental body build up and occasionally explode, affecting our body, mind, behaviours and reactions. Yog Nidra is the science of relaxation which allows us to dive down into the subconscious mind, releasing and relaxing mental tensions and establishing harmony within.

SHAVASANA
YOG NIDRA IS PERFORMED IN SHAVASANA AS THE BASE POSITION. ONE MUST BE TOTALLY COMFORTABLE AND FEEL FREE TO ADJUST THE BODY TO ONE'S SATISFACTION BEFORE STARTING

SANKALPA
RESOLUTION OR RESOLVE.
THE AIM OF THE SESSION

RELAX THE FOUR BODIES
STEP BY STEP BRING THE AWARENESS TO RELAX THE FOUR BODIES AND FIVE SENSES

FOCUS
DEEP AWARENESS OR VISUALIZATION ON THE SPECIFIC FOCUS OF THE SESSION
EXAMPLE: FOR PHYSICAL BODY, BRING AWARENESS OF MUSCLES, TISSUES, BONES, ETC.

INVITE THE DIVINE LIGHT
THIS CAN BE DONE INTERNALLY OR ALOUD. INVITE THE MOTHER'S LIGHT TO COME AND HEAL AND UPLIFT. THIS IS THE KEY TO A SUCCESSFUL YOG NIDRA

COMING OUT
GENTLY BRING FROM THE DEEP STATE BY RETURNING TO THE BODY AND SIT UP

How to Transform Bad Habits

- Bad habits are of the Apara or un-transformed nature
- Any action or habit that leads to a loss of energy is a bad habit. Consequently, good habits will generate energy.
- The use of asanas, pranayama, mantras, meditation, techniques of observation and awareness help transform bad habits without pressure, stress or the need for willpower.

Bad Habits of the Physical Body

Examples: Drinking alcohol, smoking, laziness, oversleeping, over eating, eating junk food, irregular evacuation of the bowels and lack of exercise

The Cause
- These habits occur more in a polluted physical body. Too many toxins lead to imbalance and a disconnection with your pure para nature which has pure habits.
- Your body does not follow the instructions of your physical body mind. This mind advises you not to drink in excess, to rise early in the morning, eat less and healthier, etc. But the physical body desires more food, more sugar, etc. These desires are the result of a build up of too many toxins.
- Animals eat enough to survive, and if not well, they will avoid food.
- If you eat meat, it is not bad, but be aware that you are eating more toxins as compared to vegetarian food. If the Apana Prana is strong, there is no problem, but if it is weak, there may be a build up of toxins. If the person's family history is of eating meat, it may be weakening to switch to a vegetarian diet suddenly.
- Bad habits lead to loss of energy in the physical body, and if it is not controlled will eventually lead to sickness or disease.

46

- Good food habits are required for physical health. Example: eating warm and fresh food (not too hot or cold) and avoiding chocolates, ice cream, cheese, etc., which pull your energy down.
- Positive habits are acquired by following your Higher being. We often know this, but are unable to follow due to the accumulation of toxins in our body.
- To cure these, we must simply keep purifying our body till it rejects bad habits automatically.

The Solution

- **Asana: Purification of the Physical Body through the practice of Asanas**
  This leads to automatic reduction of bad habits. With the transformation of your body, your habits become more positive. The communication channels between you and your higher nature are more open after purification. This can occur without the need of extra effort and is not dependent on the willpower of the individual.

- **Meditation: Through the Raja Yoga Method**
  While indulging in any bad habit, there is a loss of energy. But if you observe the four bodies and the observer while performing this activity, there is a balance of energy as the higher consciousness is switched on and there is no loss of energy. Example: For over eating, observe the desire, excitement, greed and the food energy is returned.

- **Invocation of the Divine Light: Bhakti Yoga Method**
  Once you are aware of the bad habits and it's effects, you may still feel the need for help to change this habit. In such a case, you can invoke the divine during this activity and feel that the Divine is with you at all times. Many problems can be alleviated with this attitude.

Bad Habits of the Prana Body

Examples: Reacting with anger or fear for the slightest reason, irritable reactions, restlessness, impatience, addiction, jealous reactions, etc.

The Cause

- The feeling of greediness may lead to a habit of stealing or fear. Insecurity can also lead to hoarding or other bad habits.
- Addiction: Craving for alcohol, drugs, smoking.
  In addiction, there is no balance or control, and indulgence is in excess of everything. It is an issue with Prana that also affects the physical body with the loss of energy. These along with excess shopping or requirement for luxuries at all times is due to impurities in the Prana Body.
- Lack of elasticity, i.e. inability to adjust with the atmosphere. Example: Prana is easily upset if there is a power cut, no air conditioning or heating or any lack of the regular setting leads to the person getting upset.
- A low Prana field can also lead to no control over one's temper and one can easily get angry, leading to more loss of energy.
- Fear and Paranoia: Many people react with fear or paranoia because of impurities in the form of unexpressed emotional energy pockets and lack of connection with the Divine. Example: Fear of Swine flu or disease, or paranoia over a situation that has not yet happened but may be a possibility in the future.
- Low Prana of impurities in the Prana Body can lead to diseases such as diabetes, problems in the reproductive organs, allergies, inflammatory diseases such as asthma, rheumatoid arthritis, etc.
- Crime: In severe cases it can lead to criminal behaviour. Murderers, rapists, etc; have very polluted Prana Bodies. Their energy is vibrating at a lower consciousness.

• Pranayama: Purification of the Prana Body

Practice of Pranayama and asana helps release pockets of stuck energy in the Prana Body. Unexpressed emotions are released through these techniques, leading to high energy or the expansion of Prana. Pure Prana is activated which leads to more positive habits, less desire and a stronger willpower is developed.

• Meditation and Observation

Helps to balance the prana body

• Invocation of the Divine Light: Bhakti Yoga Method

Invocation of the Divine Light helps overcome bad habits.

The last two methods combined can help transform bad habits. First observe yourself in the situation, become aware of your habit. This will make the situation more comfortable or bearable. After this, surrender your habit to the divine. For example: Drinking alcohol with awareness will not lead to addiction to alcohol. Once you succumb to the habit, your energy goes down, but with awareness, the Higher Para consciousness activates and you have the help and presence of the Divine.

Bad Habits of the Mental Body

Examples: Feelings of inferiority or superiority, too much thinking of the past or the future (i.e not activating or trusting your own intuitive guidance power), Negative Thinking.

The Cause
- Being fickle minded or restless is a result of Mental Prana imbalance.
- Negative thinking or Worrying: In extreme cases this may lead to over imagining problems or paranoia (sickness of the mental body). A doubting mind (psychic body is also involved) is always in the past (habit of remembering past situations and unable to let go) or the mind is in the future (the habit of day dreaming, planning consistently, unconsciously thinking of the future). This is a bad habit of the mind and most of us are unable to stay in the present.
- No satisfaction in spite of having everything is another bad habit of the mental body.
- Lack of Mental will or purpose: One is unable to achieve targets due to lack of concentration and consistency. Lack of willpower also means that the lower vital is polluted.
- Lack of confidence in oneself: being too dependent on others advice, unable to make decisions due to lack of own guidance power.
- An imbalance in the mental prana occurs when you don't know "who you are". Getting attached to the mental image of the "ego self". Thinking you have lots of knowledge, thinking you are powerful or rich, is a sign of a strong ego. Power comes from the centre of the universe. For true power of wisdom to be activated, you must observe directly, without past experience getting in the way of true knowledge.
- Sole interest in the accumulation of power and wealth: This is a bad habit of the mental body. Whether the thoughts are positive or negative, this is basically a preoccupation of the ego, which is the false mental being and holds back

one's spiritual progress. All energy is pulled down into impure mental, away from the pure mental being. Ego mind is constantly thinking about power, wealth, fame, etc., for yourself or your own family or possessions. "Observing the observer" and watching one's thoughts and reactions is a process that switches on the higher consciousness of the Para/Pure mental being. There is an immediate shift of consciousness as one steps back and observes oneself in all situations. You realize that you are a part of the universal play and the intricate connection with the universe, which leads to self-realization and oneness of being. This in turn, dissolves the ego being and awakens the true being, you realize who you are. This is the transformation of the mental energy field, and true knowledge and guidance power is now available as you observe fully remaining in the present. Inviting the Divine light into the mental energy field can also lead to change the consciousness.

The Solution
• Mantra and Yog Nidra
Asana leads to only 10% purification of the mental body. Mantra is a very effective way to cleanse the mental being along with Yog Nidra.

• Meditation: Static and Dynamic
This is a Raja Yoga technique. The power to observe increases and inner wisdom is not dependent on educational knowledge or experiences of the outer Mind which must switch off. Thoughts must be silent first. The higher intelligence is waiting to live in the present.

• Invocation of the Divine Light: Bhakti Yoga Method
Keep the heart open to the Divine. Ask for higher positive support and you will always receive help. Trust and faith will receive guidance power and right answers. Surrender to the Divine.

Bad Habits of the Psychic Body

Examples: Unkind, selfish, unhelpful, cruel.

The Cause

- Too many expectations, conditions, attachments are bad habits of the psychic body and these lead to much disappointment and pain, resulting in a loss of energy from the psychic body.
- Having no faith or trust: Doubting the person you love. Suspicion, wanting to know where they are, or even doubting whether your love will be returned.
- Attachments where the heart is involved, such as my country, my job, my religion, my god etc. involve the un-transformed psychic being and are bad habits resulting from too much attachment.
- If Day dreaming is one's occupation, means the heart is not 100% involved and the mind is else where. If there is no integral presence in the work, it remains incomplete and cannot have success. Integral presence means that the body, prana, mind and heart are all involved simultaneously. Example: If one is at work and thinking of the child, only 20% energy is at work, and little success is possible. When you are with the child, remain fully conscious, involved and stay present.
- Habit of leaving your life to the divine with no effort on your part and blaming god or destiny or bad luck for one's suffering. If the heart is divided, it cannot receive divine help. Awareness is required.
- Wanting to control your children, spouse, etc., having expectations of them or anyone else.
- If someone is unkind, selfish, unhelpful, cruel, means that their heart is blocked due to pollution of the psychic body.

The Solution
• Mantra
Purification of the psychic body can be performed with chanting invocation mantra, Om Ma and bhramari.

• Meditation and Observation
Bad habits can be transformed with awareness of the psychic behavioural patterns or habits.

• Open to the Divine Light
Offer bad habits to the supreme mother for help. Cultivate an attitude of surrender. Right attitude and intentions also help. Offering oneself as an instrument for the divine, dissolves the ego immediately.

CONCLUSION
When there are too many toxins in the physical and prana bodies, you will attract bad habits. When these bodies start to purify with the practice of yoga techniques, prana (life energy) is generated, expanded and can filter through to all four bodies. Automatically and with awareness you will maintain your energy and level of consciousness. Example: if you occasionally drink wine or are tempted to indulge in any activity that leads to loss of energy, it will not be a problem. And also since your prana is purified, you attract positive habits. With Higher awareness, the higher para consciousness helps us. With the help and presence of the Divine, you can deal with problems and tackle habits with an integral practice of yoga and meditation, and without extra stress, enter the joyful path of life.

Mantras

- Mantras create sound vibrations that have a relaxing and healing effect on all four aspects of our being. They calm the mind, creating peace, tranquillity and stillness and hence create space for energy to rise.
- Certain Mantras have a specific purpose and function as will be elaborated ahead.

Invocation Mantra

Om

Ananda mayee
Translation: She, the Delight
(We invoke supreme bliss into our four bodies)

Chaitanya mayee
Translation: She, the Consciousness
(We invoke awakened supreme consciousness into our four bodies)

Satya mayee
Translation: She, the Truth
(We invoke supreme truth into our four bodies)

Paramee
Translation: She, the Supreme
(Eternally)

All practice of Transformational Yoga begins and ends with the invocation mantra, which generates super-consciousness related energy. Invite the Divine Mother's Light to come and guide the practice improves the experience tremendously and brings unto you the grace and light of the Universe.

The Mantra also creates an energy field around the practitioner and the surroundings, creating a protective field to keep away disruptive forces, protect and cleanse the atmosphere.

To invoke The Mother's Presence is the most important aspect of the practice as it connects the practitioner to the Universal Force and invokes The Mother's Grace and blessings.

Chakra Mantras

The following mantras should be used as part of the purification routine, and supports the pranayama, asanas and chanting.

Each mantra to be repeated 3 times, whilst observing the vibrations created by the sound, starting with the relaxation mantras, followed by the cleansing mantras and lastly the activation mantras.

Chakra	Relaxation	Cleaning	Activation
MOOLADHARA	SA	LAM	OM LAM MA
SWADISHTHANA	RE	VAM	OM VAM MA
MANIPURA	GA	RAM	OM RAM MA
ANAHATA	MA	YAM	OM YAM MA
VISHUDDHI	PA	HAM	OM HAM MA
AJNA	DHA	CHAM	OM CHAM MA
SAHASRARA	NI	SRI	OM SRI MA

The mantras are very powerful and effective as they work on all 4 bodies and all 7 Chakras simultaneously. The above mentioned mantras are often a base used by different traditions of yoga and tantra in order to prepare for Higher practices.

Element Mantras

The Element Mantras help transform the 5 elements, both, within us and the environment surrounding us. The 5 elements are: earth, water, fire, air and space.

Each line to be repeated 3 times:

Om Prithvi Namaha
(Earth - Mooladhara Chakra)

Om Mahasarswati Namaha
(Transformed Earth - Sahasrara Chakra)

Om Samudrai Namaha
(Water - Swadishthana Chakra)

Om Mahalaxmi Namaha
(Transformed Water - Ajna Chakra)

Om Agni Namaha
(Fire - Manipur Chakra)

Om Mahakali Namaha
(Transformed Fire - Vishuddhi Chakra)

Om Vayu Namaha
(Air - Lower Anahata Chakra)

Om Maheshwari Namaha
(Transformed Air - Higher Anahata Chakra)

Om Aakashai Namaha
(Space Element)

Om Aditi Namaha
(Transformed Space Element)

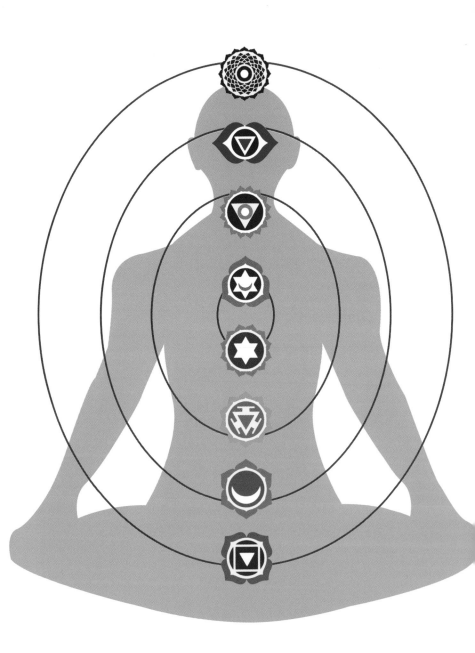

Pranayama

Activate the five pranas in the same way as the usual Transformational Yoga practice before carrying out the asanas.

(i) Maha Prana (chest breathing) x 5

Place your left hand on the upper chest, right hand over the left; inhale through the nose, hold breath for a count of 20, then exhale gently through the nose, contracting the chest.

(ii) Apana Prana (stomach breathing) x 5

Place your left hand on your tummy, then your right hand over your left; inhale slowly through your nose whilst expanding your belly, then hold for a count of 10. Exhale through your nose, while pressing down on your stomach as it contracts.

(iii) Samana Prana (kappalbhati breathing) x 25 x 2

Note: must be done on an empty stomach. Breath out, then take a deep breath in, and forcibly exhale through the nose 20 times in short sharp breaths, with the inhalation being allowed to happen passively between exhales. Put your hands on your abdomen to feel the way in which the abdominal muscles contract to force out the air.

(iv) Udana Prana (head breathing) x 5

Raise your arms and place your right hand on the back of your head, covered with your left hand. Breathe deeply through your nose, expanding your chest up and out. Hold for a count of 10, then exhale slowly through the mouth.

(v) Vyana Prana (nadi shodhana alternate nostril breathing) x 10

Method (alternate nostril breathing): Place your right thumb on your right nostril, and gently inhale through the left nostril. Close your left nostril with your 3rd finger, and release the thumb from the right nostril so that you can exhale gently through it. Inhale through the right nostril, then close it with your thumb so that you can exhale through the left. This is one round.

Asanas

Asana: Chakra Activation Set

Please note: while it is important to push one's limits and try and hold longer in each posture, do not force yourself to remain in postures, rather try and listen to your inner guidance to see how long each aspect of the practice must be performed. With time, duration, flexibility, etc. will automatically increase in a harmonious manner.

Carry out the chakra set of 10 asanas (see following pages) in 4 stages:

> **Stage 1:**
> **Purification of Physical Body (Mooladhara Chakra)**
>
> For each asana in the set, first inhale and stretch, then exhale as you move in to the pose. Hold the stretch, relax the breath, and observe the areas of pressure – both the intensity and location, noticing any particular areas of discomfort or pain. Concentrate and focus the mind on these areas, where toxins or impure energy pockets remain. As the pressure or pain starts to ease, these toxins are released. Hold the stretch for as long as you feel it is necessary (5 to 10 minutes as a guide), continuing to focus your mind on all areas of your body where pain is.

Stage 2:
Purification of Prana Body (Swadishtana Chakra)

Assume the asana or posture. Hold the stretch as before, and this time carry out kapalbhati pranayama, not too forcefully (20 - 30% force), carrying on for at least 30 breaths, more if you feel it is beneficial. Maintain your awareness of the purification process, keeping your mind focussed on your prana body. When you are ready, then release, breathing in and stretching, then breathing out as you come back to the starting position. Repeat this for each asana in the sequence.

Stage 3:
Purification of Mental Body (Manipura Chakra)

Assume the asana or posture, holding the stretch as before, and this time practice bhramari pranayama (hummingbee's breath - inhale fully through the nose, exhale through the nose while making a deep, steady humming sound). Repeat the bhramari several times, being aware of the gentle vibrations you experience, and maintaining your focus on your mental body and on the purification process. When you are ready release, breathe in and stretch, then breath out as you come back to the starting position.

Stage 4:
Purification of Psychic Body (Anahata Chakra)

Assume the asana or posture, holding the stretch as before, and this time practice the mantra **"Om Ma"**. Repeat **"Om Ma"** several times, being aware of the gentle vibrations you experience, and maintaining your focus on your heart and on the purification process. When you are ready, release, breathe in and stretch, then breath out as you come back to the starting position.

(i) Paschimotanasana (seated forward bend)

Sit with legs stretched in front of you, feet about 18 inches apart. Raise your arms whilst inhaling and stretch them above your head, then exhale and bend forward from the hip, reaching your hands towards your feet.

Physical body: Strengthens the spine, opens the muscles in the legs, makes the digestive system and sex organs healthy, increases generation of new cells, generates the 90% latent energy in Mooladhara.

Prana body: Stimulates Apana Prana and Samana Prana.

Mental body: Calms the nervous system, gives peace and mental clarity.

Psychic body: Induces peace and balance.

Spiritual body: Stimulates Sushumna nadi, Mooladhara Chakra and Kundalini Shakti.

(ii) Janu Sirshasana (head to knee pose)

Sit with legs stretched forward and feet as wide apart as you can; bend your left leg, and bring your left foot in towards your right knee. Rest your left hand on your left knee, then lift your right hand whist inhaling, and exhale while reaching down to touch your right foot.

Physical body: Strengthens the spine, opens the muscles in the legs, makes the digestive system and sex organs healthy, increases generation of new cells, generates the 90% latent energy in Swadishtana.

Prana body: Stimulates Apana Prana and Samana Prana and Maha Prana.

Mental body: Calms the nervous system, gives peace and mental clarity.

Psychic body: Induces peace and balance.

Spiritual body: Stimulates Pingala nadi, Swadishthana Chakra and Kundalini Shakti.

(iii) Janu Sirshasana (head to knee pose)

Return to centre and repeat on left side.

Physical body: Strengthens the spine, stimulates the nervous system, good for stomach and digestive system, increases generation of new cells, generates the 90% latent energy in Manipura.

Prana body: Stimulates Apana Prana and Samana Prana and Maha Prana.

Mental body: Calms the mind, gives peace, mental clarity and right guidance power.

Psychic body: Induces peace and balance, and more open to love.

Spiritual body: Stimulates Ida nadi, Manipura Chakra and Kundalini Shakti.

(iv) Pada Prasar Paschimottanasana (back stretch)

As for first back stretch, but this time with legs as wide apart as possible.

Physical body: Strengthens the spine, opens the muscles in the legs, makes the respiratory system, digestive system and reproductive system, healthy. Increases generation of new cells, generates the 90% latent energy in Mooladhara.

Prana body: Stimulates Apana Prana and Samana Prana, Maha Prana, Udana Prana and Vyana.

Mental body: Calms the nervous system, gives peace, mental clarity and focus.

Psychic body: Induces peace and balance.

Spiritual body: Stimulates Ida, Pingala and Sushumna nadis, all 7 chakras and Kundalini Shakti.

(v) Titali asana (butterfly pose)

Still sitting, bend your knees and bring your feet together so that the soles are touching; hold your feet and move your knees gently up and down 30 - 40 times, like a butterfly flapping its wings. Stay in position, bend forward over your feet whilst exhaling.

Physical body: Strengthens the spine, opens the muscles in the inner thighs, makes the digestive system and sex organs healthy, increases generation of new cells, generates the 90% latent energy in Mooladhara.

Prana body: Stimulates Apana Prana.

Mental body: Calms the nervous system, gives peace and mental clarity.

Psychic body: Induces peace and balance.

Spiritual body: Stimulates Sushumna nadi, Mooladhara Chakra and Kundalini Shakti.

(vi) Shashankasana (child pose)

Kneel on the mat, and clasp your hands behind your back, holding your right wrist with your left hand. Inhale, then lean forward so that your forehead comes down to the mat, keeping your hands behind your back, and your buttocks resting on your heels.

Physical body: Strengthens the spine and back, opens the muscles in the legs, makes the digestive system and sex organs healthy, gives better skin, helps reduce PMS and Menopause related issues, increases generation of new cells, generates the 90% latent energy in Mooladhara and swadishthana.

Prana body: Stimulates Apana Prana, Samana Prana and Maha Prana.

Mental body: Calms the nervous system, gives peace and mental clarity.

Psychic body: Induces peace and balance.

Spiritual body: Stimulates all 7 chakras and Kundalini Shakti.

(vii) Ushtrasana (camel pose)

Kneel up, so that your trunk is off the floor, as if your are standing on your knees. Place your hands behind your hips, fingers pointing down, so that your are supporting your back, inhale, and then exhale whilst leaning as far back as you can manage. If you are able to, you can reach further back, placing your hands behind you on your heels to give balance.

Physical body: Strengthens the spine, opens the heart, lungs and throat region, balances the thyroid gland, and controls hunger and thirst.

Prana body: Stimulates Samana, Maha and Udana Prana.

Mental body: Calms the nervous system, gives peace, mental clarity and right guidance.

Psychic body: Induces peace and balance

Spiritual body: Stimulates Sushumna nadi, and higher chakras.

(viii) Marjari Asana (cat posture)

Get on hands and knees, keeping knees slightly apart so you are balanced. Inhale, and raise your head so you are looking up, arch your spine downwards so that it is in a concave shape, then exhale while lowering your head and arching your back like a cat. Repeat this movement 2 or 3 times to increase flexibility, then move into the first position and hold. First posture, look ahead, arch spine down so it is in a concave shape.

Physical body: Strengthens the spine, tones the buttocks, improves blood circulation, makes the digestive system and sex organs healthy.

Prana body: Stimulates Apana Prana and Samana Prana.

Mental body: Calms the nervous system, gives peace and mental clarity.

Psychic body: Induces peace and balance

Spiritual body: Stimulates Sushumna nadi, Mooladhara, Swadishthana, Manipura and Anahata Chakras.

(ix) Marjari Asana (cat posture)

Second posture, head down, back arched upwards in convex shape.

Physical body: Strengthens the spine, balances the thyroid gland, helps in spondylitis, makes the digestive system and sex organs healthy, increases generation of new cells, generates the 90% latent energy in Mooladhara.

Prana body: Stimulates Samana, Maha, Udana Prana and Vyana.

Mental body: Calms the nervous system, gives peace, mental clarity and right guidance.

Psychic body: Induces peace and balance.

Spiritual body: Stimulates Sushumna nadi, Manipura, Anahata, Vishuddhi and all higher Chakras.

(x) Parvatasana (mountain pose)

Keeping your hands on the floor as for the cat pose, straighten your knees and stand onto your feet, keeping your head lowered and your back arched, and—if you can—straighten your legs and stand on the soles of your feet with your feet flat to the ground.

Physical body: Increases blood circulation to the brain, strengthens the spine, legs, calf and shoulder muscles, increases overall strength.

Prana body: Apana, Samana, Maha, Udana and Vyana Prana.

Mental body: Calms the nervous system, gives peace and mental clarity.

Psychic body: Induces peace and balance.

Spiritual body: Provides connection of Sahasrara to Mooladhara Chakra.

Meditation

Meditation is any method that creates harmony and peace, while giving us an experience of our Para nature. In true meditation, the Ego dissolves, there is Transformation and the consciousness is lifted.

- Energy usually stabilizes in the lower chakras, but it is brought upwards through Self-Observation when the para nature is turned on. This results in a more positive, elastic nature.

- Types of Meditation: Meditation can be Static (sitting in one place) or Dynamic. Any action performed with awareness and an aspiration towards higher self can become a dynamic meditation, such as a walk or playing music, etc.

- **Raja Yoga Meditation:** Uses wisdom-oriented techniques and is concentrated in the 3rd chakra or the mental body.
- **Bhakti Yoga Meditation:** is heart-oriented meditation and is connected with the 4th chakra. It leads to psychic awakening.
- **Karma Yoga Meditation:** is action-oriented meditation
- **Sankia (Gyana) Yoga:** works with higher chakras and concentrates on the divine within us. Listen to and feel the peace inside, follow the inner guru and enlightenment happens. It leads to respect the Divine within and in everybody else.

- **Observation:** It is the key to a successful meditation. When in a difficult situation, stop and observe before you blindly react. This gives you time to switch into your para body and immediately transforms the negative energy into positive wisdom. Normally we react to outside influences in a state of unconsciousness, but with self-awareness we are able to jump into higher consciousness.

- **Dharana:** Concentration is the first step to meditation. Focusing on something on the outside is Dharana or concentration, while when the focus shifts within oneself, it becomes meditation. Dharana is a good way for people to be introduced to meditation.

- **Dhyana:** it involves observation and awareness of the four bodies.
  - ◊ **Physical Body:** relax the muscles, spine and feel the energy flow.
  - ◊ **Prana Body:** watch the breath, blind emotions and surrender desires to the divine.
  - ◊ **Mental Body:** watching the thoughts, staying in the present and surrendering the ego.
  - ◊ **Psychic Body:** look at what is in your heart and allow unconditional love to enter.

- **Ask your self:** Who is my true self? What is my purpose here?

- **Samadhi:** This state is the goal- dynamic meditation with constant awareness throughout life

- **The Internal Law**
  - ◊ Let go of the ego in order to learn, be open and innocent like a child, then the true self awakens.
  - ◊ Thinking you already know everything is a big block in the mental body.
  - ◊ Strive to be an endless learner and open new dimensions. The inner journey never ends.
  - ◊ Good within attracts good without, same for the bad.

Transformational Integral Meditation Education (TIME)

1. RELAX
PHYSICAL BODY

2. RELAX
PRANA BODY
(BREATH)

9. OBSERVE
WHO IS THE
OBSERVER

3. RELAX
MENTAL BODY
(THOUGHTS/MIND,
STOMACH AREA)

8. OBSERVE
PSYCHIC BODY

4. RELAX
PSYCHIC BODY
(HEART/LUNGS,
CHEST/
REGION)

7. OBSERVE
MENTAL BODY

6. OBSERVE
PRANA BODY

5. OBSERVE
PHYSICAL BODY

---

1. RELAX YOUR PHYSICAL BODY   **2. RELAX YOUR BREATH (VITAL)**

3. RELAX YOUR MIND   **4. RELAX YOUR HEART**

5. OBSERVE YOUR PHYSICAL BODY **6. OBSERVE YOUR BREATH (VITAL)**

7. OBSERVE YOUR MIND   **8. OBSERVE YOUR HEART**

9. OBSERVE YOUR TRUE SELF   **10. REPEAT**

Sequence: How to Practice

Self-purification includes the following elements:

- Invocation mantra
- Chakra mantras
- Pranayama
- Bandhas
- Sequence of asanas
- Yog Nidra
- Meditation
- Invocation mantra

Each individual is different, and time taken varies for each individual. Ideally, the most effective way to achieve this is to undertake a complete retreat from everyday life until you feel you have completed it. Of course, for most people this is not practical or feasible, and the routine will need to be incorporated into your life in a way which will work for you. How you go about this will depend on your own personal circumstances, for example, you might be able to spend one day per week, or one day per month; alternatively you may be able to spend one or two weekends per month. The frequency affects the length of time you will take to complete the purification—so if you have less time to spend on it, you will need to accept that it could take up to six months or a year.

For any further help, support or guidance please feel free to contact us on our website:

www.srimatransformationalyoga.com

Of one thing you can be sure -
your future is in your hands.
You will become the man you
want to be and the higher your
ideal and your aspiration, the
higher will be your realization,
but you must never forget
your true aim in life.

- The Mother

SWAMI VIDYANAND
Founder and Director
Country: India
srima.swami@gmail.com
+91-9810670711

Name: Arjun Goswami
Country: India
Co-Director, Executive Director
yogawitharjun@gmail.com

Name: Srdjan Jovanovic
Co-Director
Country: Serbia
srdjanjovanovic.sj@gmail.com

Name: Utkarsh Sanjanwala
Spiritual Name: Uttar Kashi
Co-Director
Country: New Zealand/India
meetutkarsh@gmail.com

Name: Vandana Wadera
Spiritual Name: Yogini Aditi
Co-Director
Country: India/UK
vandanawadera@hotmail.com

Name: Katy Robinson
Spiritual Name: Krishna Kali
Co-Director
Country: UK
allthatkatydid@gmail.com

Name: Maria Arati
Spiritual Name: Divya Agni
Co-Director
Country: India
mariaselvig@gmail.com

Name: Hollis Antler
Spiritual Name: Surya Mukhi
Co-Director
County: USA
antler.hollis@yahoo.com

Name: Solange
Spiritual Name: Ganga
Country: France
gangasoul@gmail.com

Name: Michelle Kaminski
Co-Director
County: Italy
yogaallianceeurope@gmail.com

Name: Diana Button
Spiritual Name: Prem Agni
County: Italy
diana.button@yahoo.it

Name: Irene Branders
Co-Director
Country: South Africaireen.
branders39@gmail.com

Name: Hannah Derechsel
Spiritual Name: Brahma Jyoti
Country: Italy
hanna.drechsel@gmail.com

Name: Lim Kang
Spiritual Name: Divya Murti
Co-Director
Country: Singapore
limkang@me.com

Name: Emily Gilchrist
Spiritual Name: Satya Murti
Country: France/UK
emilyogagilchrist@gmail.com

Name: Maria Lucas
Spiritual Name: Nirvana
Country: Argentina
chikitamaria@yahoo.com

Name: Sonia Karkare
Spiritual Name: Savitri
Country: India
soniaskeukare@gmail.com

Name: Matthew Newsome
Spiritual Name: Vashisht
Country: France/UK
matthewjamesnewsome@gmail.com

Name: Sudevi Sundari
Spiritual Name: Sri Kumari
Country: Hongkong / Austral
yogawithsudevi@hotmail.com

Name: Sharon O'Niell
Spiritual Name: Sri Radha
Country: Ireland
oneillsharon22@gmail.com

Name: Elanora
Country: Italy
lola_mergo@yahoo.it

Name: Pieter Assendelft
Spiritual Name: Vishwa Mitra
Country: France
quartero@luxinet.fr

Name: Lauren Goodey
Country: United Kingdom
laurengoodey@hotmail.co.uk

Name: Julie Giacomini
Spiritual Name: Durga
Country: France
julie@dirga-ji.fr

Name: Tyler Ali
Spiritual Name: Paramhansa
County: USA
t.ghautecouture@gmail.com

Name: Dominique
Spiritual Name: Satya Mitra
Country: Italy
dominique.trauttmansdorff@gmail.com

Name: Ivana Brigliadori
Spiritual Name: Yog Sundari
Country: Italy
ivana@ivanabrigliadori.com

Name: Cécile Vieillard
Spiritual Name: Atma Shakti
Country: France
vieillard.cecile@free.fr

Name: Irene van Gent
Country: Holland
irenevangent@hotmail.com

Name: Klara Nagy
Country: Europe
klaranagy99@gmail.com

Name: Ness
Spiritual Name: Agni
Country: South Africa
neshbrzeska@yahoo.com

Name: Carolina
Country: Germany
tapp_carolina@web.de

Name: Shalini
Country: Congo
shalini@iburstafrica.com

• • •